Fun with Pets

by
Laurel Hicks
and
Carolyn Rowlinson

Illustrated by
Amy Tedder
with Michelle Johnson, Lauren Pope,
Sonya Wilson

A Beka Book® Pensacola, FL 32523-9100
an affiliate of PENSACOLA CHRISTIAN COLLEGE®

Contents

Say the sounds that these letters make.

A a

apple *Aa*

F f

fox *Ff*

S s

sun *Ss*

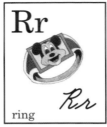

R r

ring *Rr*

T t

table *Tt*

M m

milk *Mm*

Say the blends and then make words.

Read the words.

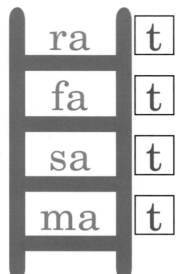

ra	t
fa	t
sa	t
ma	t

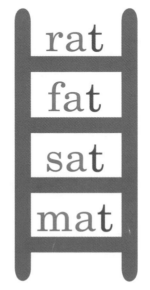

rat
fat
sat
mat

You may need help with these words:

is

Sometimes *s* says "z."

on

the

The sight word **the** is pronounced "thŭ."

a

The sight word **a** is pronounced "ŭ."

Read the phrases.

the rat	the mat	the fat rat

the rat   the mat   the fat rat

Now you can read the story!

The Fat Rat

The rat is fat.

The rat sat.

The fat rat sat on
the mat.

The fat rat sat on the mat.

Say the sounds.

Ss  sun *Ss*	**Tt**  table *Tt*	**Mm**  milk *Mm*
Bb  bell *Bb*	**Dd**  dog *Dd*	**Hh**  horse *Hh*

Say the blends and then make words.

sa   t

ba   d

ha   m

Read the words.

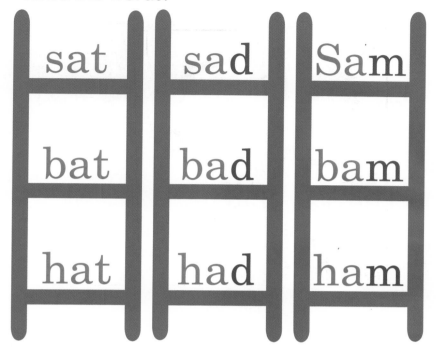

sat	sad	Sam
bat	bad	bam
hat	had	ham

Read the phrases.

a rat	*a rat*
a hat	*a hat*
a bat	*a bat*
a ham	*a ham*

Now finish the story!

The rat had
a bat.

The rat had
a hat.

Bad rat! Sad Sam!

The rat had a ham.

Bad rat!

Bam!

When you finish reading, color this picture!

Read the rhyming words.

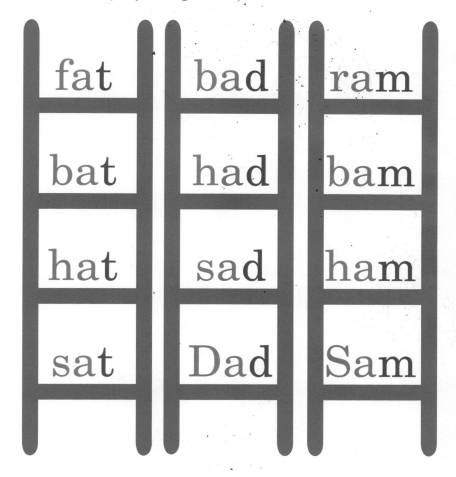

fat	bad	ram
bat	had	bam
hat	sad	ham
sat	Dad	Sam

Read the phrases.

a mat	the bat
on the hat	on the ham

Say the sounds.

A a apple *Aa*	**Cc** cat *Cc*	**Pp** pig *Pp*
Ll lamp *Ll*	**Bb** bell *Bb*	**Hh** horse *Hh*
Gg goat *Gg*	**Nn** nest *Nn*	

You may need help with this word:

sack

ck says "k."

Read the words.

cat	can	cap
sat	sag	sack
pat	pan	fan

You may need help with these words:

the	a
is	in

Read the phrases.

in the can   in a pan

in the can   in a pan

Pat's Cat

Pat had a cat.

The cat sat in Pat's lap.

"Pat's cat" means that the cat belongs to Pat.

Pat's cat can lap.

Pat's cat can nap.

Pat's cat had a hat.

The hat is a cap.

Pat's cat can tap the cap.

Pat's cat had a bag.

A bag is a sack.

Pat's cat can pat the sack.

The sack can sag.

Pat the sack, cat.

Pat's cat sat in the sack.

The cat sat and sat and sat.

Pat's cat can tag the fat rat.

The rat ran!

The cat sat in a pan.

A tack is in the pan.

The cat ran!

When you finish reading, color this picture!

Read the rhyming words.

lap	cap	tap	rap
can	ran	pan	fan
bag	tag	sag	rag
hat	pat	fat	cat

Say the sounds and clue words.

Ee

elephant

Ww

wagon

Yy

yarn

Say the blends and then make words.

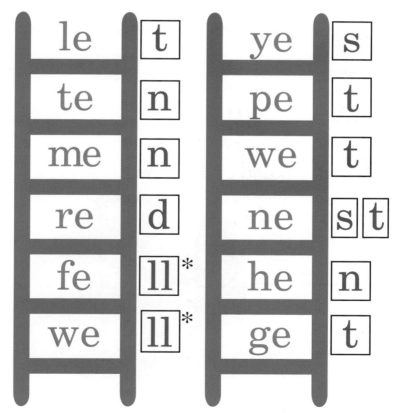

le	t
te	n
me	n
re	d
fe	ll*
we	ll*

ye	s
pe	t
we	t
ne	st
he	n
ge	t

*When a consonant is doubled at the end of a word, it says its sound only once.

24

Read the phrases.

a pet	a nest	a pan

the hen	the sack	the man

a red hen

a wet mess

the tan sack

the tan sack

The *s* at the end of these words says "z."

has

is

eggs

Ted's Mess

Ted has a pet.

The pet is a red hen.

Red Hen has a nest.

Red Hen sat on the nest.

Red Hen had ten eggs
in the nest.

Ted, get Dad!

Tell Dad Red Hen has a
nest.

Tell Dad the nest has eggs.

Yes, Ted can tell Dad.

Let Ted get
the tan
sack.

Get the ten eggs, Ted.

Ted ran fast.

Ted fell on the sack.

Ted had a wet mess.

Yes, a mess!

A bad, sad mess!

Get the rag, Ted.

Get a pan.

Pat at the mess.

Yes!

When you finish reading, color this picture!

Read the rhyming words.

let	pet	wet	get
can	ran	tan	pan

Draw lines to match the rhyming words.

hen   Ted

mess   ten

fell   yes

red   tell

Say the sounds.

Indian   *Ii*

kite   *Kk*

Say the blends and then make words.

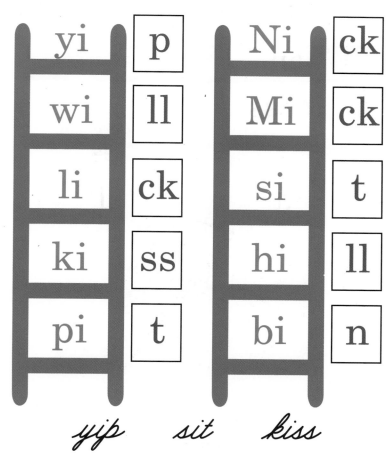

yi	p
wi	ll
li	ck
ki	ss
pi	t

Ni	ck
Mi	ck
si	t
hi	ll
bi	n

yip   sit   kiss

Read the words.

Nick	Mick	sick
yip	yes	yell
will	wet	wag
miss	kiss	Kip
it	is	in	on

Kip

Nick and Mick sit.

Nick is sad.

Mick is sad.

Nick and Mick miss Kip.

Nick and Mick yell.

Kip! Kip!

Is Kip on the hill?

Is Kip in the pit?

Is Kip sick?

Yip, yip!

It is Kip.

Kip hid in the big bin.

Kip had a nap.

Kip will lick Mick.

Kip will wag.

Kip will kiss Nick.

Nick gets a big, wet kiss.

Nick will let Kip lick him.

Nick and Mick will pet Kip.

Sit, Kip, sit!

Kip sat.

When you finish reading, color this picture!

41

Say the sounds and clue words.

Oo  ostrich *Oo*	**Uu**  umbrella *Uu*

Jj  jar *Jj*	**Vv**  violin *Vv*	**Xx**  "ks" fox box ax *Xx*

Read the words.

top	hop	box
jug	sup	fun
Ben	wet	vet
fix	tan	van

Bob

Bob is big.

Bob is six.

Bob can
  hop.

Bob can box.

Bob can jog
  and
  Bob can hit.

Bob is big.

Bob has jobs.

Bob can mop and

Bob can dig.

Bob can dock.

Bob can fix a lock.

Bob fed
the dog.

Bob fed
the hen.

Bob fed the pig.

Bob is big.

Bob will kiss Mom.

When you finish reading, color this picture!

Draw a line from the sentence to the picture that goes with it.

Bob can jog.

Bob can dig.

Bob fed the hen.

Pug

Pug is just a pup.

Pug is not as big
    as a cat.

Pug can fit in a cup.

The bun is as big as Pug.

Jan will pet Pug.

Jan will hug Pug.

Pug will kiss Jan.

Pug has a big, wet kiss.

Pug got a bug.

The bug is not as big
    as Pug.

The bug has six red legs.

Pug yips at the bug.

Is Puff as big as Pug?

Pug will run!

Pug dug in the mud.

Pug is a mess!

Run, Jan.

Fill the cup.

The cup is Pug's tub.

Pug got wet in the cup.

Pug got a rub.

Pug got a hug.

Pug is a fun pet!

When you finish reading, color this picture!

Tell God, Ben

The cat fell in the well.

The cat got wet.

Tell Dad, Ben.

Dad can help.

Ben did tell Dad.

Dad got a net.

Dad did help.

The cat got a hug.

Ben fell.

Ben got a nick.

Tell Mom, Ben.

Mom can help.

Ben did tell Mom.

Ben got a kiss.

Mom did help.

Mom got a hug.

Ben did it.

Ben bent the van.

Ben felt sad.

Tell God, Ben.

God can help.

Ben did tell God.

Ben got a hug.

Ben got a kiss.

Ben felt glad.

When you finish reading, color this picture!

Draw a line from the sentence to the picture that goes with it.

Ben will tell Dad.

The cat got a hug.

Ben will tell God.

Read the names. Tell who did what.

Ben	Kip	Mick	Nick
God	Sam	Pat	Ted
Bob		Pug	Puff
Mom			Dad

Draw a line from the sentence to the picture that goes with it.

The rat has Sam's hat.

Ted's pet is a hen.

Ted got the tan sack.

Kip will lick Mick.

Say the sounds.

Read the words.

quack	quick

zip	zag	Zack

quill	quiz

Zack

Zack is a big duck.

Zack has a bill.

Zack can swim and
    quack.

"Quack, quack, quack!"

Quick, Zack.

Get the fat red bug.

Zig-zag went the bug.

Zap! Zack got it!

"Quack, quack, quack!"

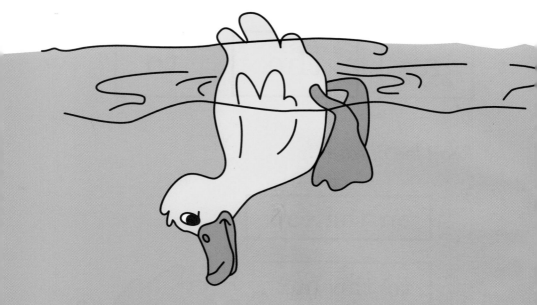

Get in the pond, Zack.

Dip and swim.

Swim and dip.

Zack is a wet duck.

A quick wet duck is a
        fun pet!

Read the sight words.

a	the	to

Read the phrases.

on the cap

to the box

in a cup

to a hill

at a pic/nic

to the pond

ă   ě   ĭ   ŏ   ŭ

Listen to the rule. Read the words.

> When there is one vowel in a word, the vowel usually says its short sound. We mark it with a smile.

căt	pĭg	hěn
dŏg	dŭck	blăck

Mark the vowels. Read the words.

jăm	lĭck	bŭn
rěst	hělp	hŏt
rŭn	wěnt	zĭp

Ann Ant

Ann is a black ant.

Ann Ant has a hill.

It is an ant hill.

Ron and Deb had a
     pic/nic.

Ann went to the pic/nic.

Ann Ant ran to a bun.

Red jam is on the bun.

Lick, lick, lick!

Ann had jam.

Can Ann lug the big
bun to the hill?

Just a bit.

Ann will lug.

Ann will rest.

Ann will not quit.

Ann will run back to
the hill.

Ann will get help!

Ten black ants will help
Ann.

Can ten ants get the bun
and jam to the hill?

Yes, ten ants can!

Say the sound.

Aa

acorn

ay in pray

ay in pray

Listen to the rules. Read the words.

1. When there is one vowel in a word, the vowel usually says its short sound.

ă ĕ ĭ ŏ ŭ

căp Jăn păd căn

2. When there are two vowels in a word, the first vowel says its long sound, and the second vowel is silent.

ā ē ī ō ū

cāpe Jāne pāid cāne

3. The special sound **ay** says **ā**. (It usually comes at the end of a word.) **ay**

say day ray gray

Mark the vowels. Circle the special sounds. Read the words.

gāve	sāve
made	wade
ate	grain
Kate	Gail
day	may

Read the sentence.

Gail ate the cake.

Gail ate the cake.

Six Duck Eggs

A man gave Kate
    six duck eggs.

His big ducks laid the eggs.

Kate had a hen but
    not a duck.

The hen
    went to
        the eggs.

Kate let the hen sit
on the duck eggs.

"Cluck, cluck," went
the hen.

"Cluck, cluck, cluck!"

The hen sat and sat
on the duck eggs.

Peck, peck! Peck, peck!

Pop! Pop! Pop!

Pop! Pop! Pop!

Six ducks came
from the eggs.

Six ducks lay in the nest.

"Cluck, cluck," went the hen.

"Quack, quack," went the
   ducks.

"Cluck!"   "Quack!"

"Cluck!"   "Quack!"

The hen gave the ducks
      grain.

Peck, peck, peck, went
   the ducks.

The ducks ate
   and ate
      and ate.

Kate gave the ducks
names.

The black duck is Bill.

The fast duck is Swift.

The big duck is Mac.

The gray duck is
Quack-Quack.

The soft duck is Fluff.

The last duck is Jake.

"Quack, quack! Quack,
    quack!" went the six
    ducks.

"Let's wade in the lake!
    Let's play!"

"Stop! Stop!" went the hen.

"Cluck, cluck, cluck!"

But the ducks did not stop.

The six ducks ran
    to the
        lake.

In went Bill.

In went Swift.

In went Mac.

In went Quack-Quack.

In went Fluff.

In went Jake.

Dip! Swim! Dip! Swim!

The ducks swam
and swam.

Kate's six wet ducks
had fun.

Kate is glad
God made ducks.

Mark the ○ by the sentence that is true.

Ducks can swim. ○

Hens can swim. ○

A hen will cluck. ○

A duck will cluck. ○

An ant is big. ○

A dog is big. ○

A hen likes to get wet. ○

A duck likes to get wet. ○

Say the sound.

Eē

eagle Eē

e in mē

e in mē

Say the rules. Read the words.

---

1. When there is one vowel in a word, the vowel usually says its short sound.

ă ĕ ĭ ŏ ŭ

pĕt fĕd sĕt nĕt

---

2. When there are two vowels in a word, the first vowel says its long sound, and the second vowel is silent.

ā ē ī ō ū

Pēte fēed sēe nēat

---

3. When *e* is the only vowel at the end of a short word, it usually says its long sound. ē

be he me we

Mark the vowels. Circle the special sounds. Read the words.

Zēke	bēef	nēed
bēan	lean	clean
neat	leap	sleep
came	name	named
lay	say	play
he	me	we	be

Sight word: | from |

Read the sentences.

He is named Zeke.

We will be neat.

Zeke and
the Flea*

Pete has a gray cat.

He named his cat Zeke.

He made Zeke a soft bed.

Pete feeds Zeke milk and
   beef.

Zeke eats from
   Pete's hand.

*with Adorae Lester

Zeke lay in the sun and
went to sleep.

Pete came to play.

Pete can see a flea
on Zeke.

"Wake up, Zeke!
I see a
black flea.

It will hop on me.

We need to get
the flea!"

ᵃ

Hop! Hop! Hop!

Zeke sees the flea jump.

The flea is still on Zeke.

"Quick, Zeke!
Get the flea!"

Zig-zag! Zig-zag!

The flea hops and jumps.

The flea is
still
on
Zeke!

Lick, lick, lick.

Zeke licks his back and
    neck.

The flea still hops and
    jumps.

Lick, lick, lick.

Zeke licks his legs and feet.

The flea **still** hops and
    jumps.

Lick, lick, lick.

Zeke licks his tail.

The flea stops.

Zeke bit the flea.

Zeke has a wet back.

He has a wet neck.

Zeke has wet legs and feet,
and he has a wet tail.

But he got the flea!

Pete is glad he has
a clean,
neat pet.

Say the sounds.

Iī

ice cream   Iī

y in fly

y in fly

Say the rules. Read the words.

---

1. When there is one vowel in a word, the vowel usually says its short sound.

ă ĕ ĭ ŏ ŭ

Mĭck lĭck hĭd

---

2. When there are two vowels in a word, the first vowel says its long sound, and the second vowel is silent.

ā ē ī ō ū

Mīke līke hīde

---

3. Sometimes *y* acts like a vowel. When *y* is the only vowel at the end of a short word, it says ī.

my   by   fly   sty

Read the words. Mark the vowels.
Circle the special sounds.

Mike	like	likes
lie	fine	mine
my	he	play

Sight word: I

Mark the ○ by the sentence that is true.

Cats like fleas. ○
Cats like meat. ○

I can jump. ○
I can fly. ○

I Like Pigs*

My name is Mike.

I like the cats and dogs
   God made.

I like the hens and ducks
   and geese He made.

But I like the
   pigs the
      best.

*with Adorae Lester

My pet pig is fat and
　　sleek.

He likes to lie in the mud.

He will not get stuck in
　　the mud.

He just has fun in it.

He likes to play and play.

I made my pig a fine pig
   pen.

I got a pail to feed him.

He eats husks and grain.

He digs up nuts.

My pig is not a neat pet,
but he is mine,
and I like him!

I am glad God made pigs.

Say the sound.

open

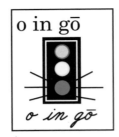

o in gō

o in gō

Say the rules. Read the words.

---

1. When there is one vowel in a word, the vowel usually says its short sound.

ă ĕ ĭ ŏ ŭ

Rŏd   Tŏdd   Jŏn   hŏps

---

2. When there are two vowels in a word, the first vowel says its long sound, and the second vowel is silent.

ā ē ī ō ū

rōad   tōad   Jōan   hōpes

---

3. When *o* is the only vowel at the end of a short word, it usually says its long sound. ō

go   so   no   yo-yo

Read the words. Mark the vowels.
Circle the special sounds.

home	roam	pole
likes	makes	tad/pole
no	go	so	Joe
lay	play	gray

Sight word: | of |

Mark the ○ by the sentence that is true.

The pig's home is a pen. ○
The pig's home is a pail. ○

Cats like to play in the mud. ○
Pigs like to play in the mud. ○

Joan's Pet Toad

Joan has a fun pet.

It is a gray toad.

A toad is like a frog.

It has bumps on its skin.

It jumps on its big back
legs.

It makes Joan smile to
see the toad
hop and
jump.

Joan made the
toad a home.

The toad sits and sits in
its home.

It likes to croak and
croak.

The toad sat in its home.

A fly went by.

"Buzz!" went the fly.

Zip! went the toad.

The toad ate it up fast.

Joan's mom likes the toad
to eat bugs and flies
so the plants will
be safe.

Joan likes to see the toad
hop and jump.

If it hops to the road, Joan
gets it back.

"No, Toad! Hop on the
grass, not on the road.
The grass is safe.
Go, Toad, go! Hop fast!"

The toad will lay eggs in
the pond.

The eggs will be
tad/poles.

And the tad/poles will be
toads.

And Joan will get lots of
pet toads to eat the
bugs on Mom's plants.

Joan's mom is glad God
made toads,
and so is Joan!

Say the sounds.

Uū

uniform *Uū*

Long *u*
can say
ū or **o͞o**.

Say the rules. Read the words.

---

1. When there is one vowel in a word, the
   vowel usually says its short sound.

   ă ĕ ĭ ŏ **ŭ**

   dŭck cŭt sŭn

---

2. When there are two vowels in a word,
   the first vowel says its long sound, and
   the second vowel is silent.

   ā ē ī ō **ū**

   Dūke cūte Sūe

Read the sight words.

| to | do | you |

| said |

Read the words. Mark the vowels.

blue   tune   Luke

plant   plants   yell   yells

like   likes   name   named

Mark the ○ by the sentences that are true.

Toads lay eggs. ○
Hens lay eggs. ○
Cats lay eggs. ○

A pig eats grain. ○
A dog eats grain. ○
A duck eats grain. ○

Duke

Luke has a pet goat.
It is not a big goat;
   it is just a kid.

It still gets sweet milk
   from Nan, its mom,
   and it likes the grass and
   leaves Luke feeds it.

Luke named his goat Duke.

Duke has a tan coat and a
cute tan tail.

Sue sees the goat.

"Will he bite me?" asks Sue.

"No, Sue," said Luke. "He
likes you. Feed him a
leaf, and you will see."

Sue held up a green leaf.

"Eat the leaf, Duke," Sue said. "Take a big bite!"

"Ma-a-a!" said Duke. "Ma-a-ma-ma!"

And he ate and ate and ate.

Sue ran and got a tin can.

"Will he eat the can?" said
Sue. "Let's try it
and see."

Sue held the tin can up to
Duke.

"Ma-a-a!
Ma-a-a!"
said
Duke.

But he did
not eat
the can.

A big toad sat in the sun
on a stone.

"Do goats eat toads?"

"No," Luke said. "Goats
eat milk and plants
but not frogs and
toads and tin cans."

Duke sees a red rose.

He sniffs the rose and takes a bite.

"No, Duke!" Luke yells.

"You must not eat Mom's rose. Eat grass and leaves, not the rose."

But Duke just ate and ate.

Sue gave Duke a red and
blue hat.

Luke gave him a bell.

The bell made a fine tune,
but the hat fell to the
grass.

"No, Duke!" cried Sue.
"Stop! Stop! Do not eat
the hat! Goats eat
milk and leaves and
grass, but not hats!"

"Ma-a-a!" said Duke.

"Ma-ma-ma-a-a!"

And he ate and
ate and
ate.

Tim Tom and Rib Rab

Tim Tom came up the
road.

He had his home on his
back.

Tim Tom did not run.

He is not fast.

Rib Rab sat by the road.

"Stop, Tim Tom, stop!"
said Rib Rab.

"I can beat you. I am
fast!"

"Rib Rab is fast!"
said the goat.

"He will beat Tim Tom,"
said the bee.

"Go, Rib Rab, go!"
cried the toad.

"Run, Tim Tom, run!"
said the ant.

"Can't you run, Tim Tom?"
said the pig.

"No," said Tim Tom.

"I can not run. I am not
fast, but I will not
stop."

Hop! Leap! Hop! Leap!
went Rib Rab.

Plod, plod, plod
went Tim Tom.

Tim Tom did not hop, but
Tim Tom did not stop.

Rib Rab **did** stop.

"Tim Tom is not fast,"
said Rib Rab. "He can
not beat me. I will
just stop and take
a rest."

Rib Rab had a nap.

He slept and slept and
    slept.

As Rib Rab slept, Tim
    Tom went past him.

Tim Tom went on and on.

He went on and on
    to the end.

"Tim Tom wins!"
said the goat.

"Tim Tom beat Rib Rab!"
said the ant.

"Tim Tom is not fast,"
cried the toad,
"but he will not stop."

"Tim Tom wins!"
    cried the goat,
    the bee, and the pig.
    "Tim Tom
        made it
            to

the end